Wheels on the Bus

The wheels on the bus go **round** and **round**,
Round and **round**, **round** and **round**.
The wheels on the bus go **round** and **round**,
All through the town.

The puddles on the road go splash splash splash,
Splash splash splash, splash splash splash.
The puddles on the road go splash splash splash,
All through the town.

The doors on the bus go **open** and **shut**,
open and **shut**, **open** and **shut**.
The doors on the bus go **open** and **shut**,
All through the town.

The parents at the bus say, "Have a nice day.

Have a nice day. Have a nice day."

The parents at the bus say, "Have a nice day,"

All through the town.

The horn on the bus goes beep beep beep,

Beep beep beep, beep beep beep.

The horn on the bus goes **beep beep beep,**

All through the town.

The people on the bus go **back** and **forth**,
Back and **forth**, **back** and **forth**.
The people on the bus go **back** and **forth**,
All through the town.

The people on the bus go **up** and **down**,
Up and **down**, **up** and **down**.
The people on the bus go **up** and **down**,
All through the town.

The kids on the bus go blah blah blah,
Blah blah blah, blah blah blah.

The kids on the bus go **blah blah blah,**
All through the town.

The driver on the bus goes shhh shhh shhh,
Shhh shhh shhh, shhh shhh shhh.

The teacher on the bus says, "Let me off! Let me off! Let me off!

The teacher on the bus says, "Let me off!"

All through the town.

The kids on the bus say, "Thanks for the ride. Thanks for the ride. Thanks for the ride." The kids on the bus say, "Thanks for the ride." And now they're all at school.